SUNBEAM DRAGONFLIES

A Little Book to Give You Hope Through Chronic Fatigue and Life in General

Trina Chapman

ARTHUR H. STOCKWELL LTD
Torrs Park, Ilfracombe, Devon, EX34 8BA
Established 1898
www.ahstockwell.co.uk

British Library Cataloguing-in-Publication Data.
A catalogue record for this book is available
from the British Library.

Arthur H. Stockwell Ltd bears no responsibility
for the accuracy of information recorded in this book.

ISBN 978-0-7223-5116-1
Printed in Great Britain by
Arthur H. Stockwell Ltd
Torrs Park   Ilfracombe
Devon EX34 8BA

PREFACE

When I began writing about my journey with ME, and the things that I have learned along the way, I was intending it to help people in the same situation as myself. What I have come to realise, listening to comments from family and friends, is that this book can help anybody.

The current global pandemic has impacted many lives, leaving so many people with chronic fatigue, anxiety and brain fog, very similar symptoms to ME. My story could help anyone who is struggling to deal with the changes and lift them back into the light.

INTRODUCTION

When I was told recently that I would write a book, I thought to myself, 'Whatever could I write a book about?'

I have been told this a few times in the past, but just pushed it to one side.

My friend Amy was telling me that she had met up with a new friend and they had done the same workshops and retreats together. They got on so well. That made me think, 'What have I got to share of interest about myself?' I have ME and can't work, so therefore have very little spare money to even go to an evening meditation group, and I felt the old 'Poor me – life's not always fair' creeping in.

Then there was a lightbulb moment. Maybe I haven't been able to do all of those things during the past thirteen years that I have been on my own spiritual ME journey, but I have been on my own pilgrimage. Along the way I have met some wonderful people whom I have learned so much from, either for free or at a very low cost.

Family, old friends and new have treated me to lunch and bought me nice things to eat, and things I need, and shared words of wisdom.

My dear friend Lynn used to put me together a box of

things that she knew I loved for Christmas each year. That meant so much to me. Now that we no longer live near to each other she sends me money to get my own treats.

Some of the best things in life are free, such as the indigo sky at dawn and dusk, sunrise and sunset.

One of the most beautiful sights that I ever saw was when there had been a real heavy downpour just as the sun was setting. It stopped and the skies cleared to show a red sunset. The tree in the garden had large drops of water still hanging from its branches. The sun reflected off them, turning them into beautiful red shiny jewels. It truly was amazing to see.

Before I started my journey I was One Big Mess!

Things happen in life, but I don't want this book to be a book about blaming people from my past. It's more about how I've found ways to help myself move forward.

The people who press our buttons are often our greatest teachers – not that we realise that at the time.

I have a lot of tools and knowledge in my toolbox that I can share.

There must be many people in my situation, where going to a workshop, meditation group or retreat is out of the question. So my book is for all of you. It hasn't cured the ME that I have, but it's helped me to stay calmer and see it as a friend rather than something to fear. I feel that I'm well on my way to recovering now.

It's almost been a gift, as I have been able to work on and release so many of my old issues and find out who I truly am.

Although my toolbox works for me, it might not do the same for everyone. Or you might think, 'Yeah, right! As if I'm doing that!'

Many a time I have thought, 'That won't work – it's not what I'm all about,' and I have totally resisted what I'm being shown, only to find months down the line it suddenly pops up again, just when it's needed! This is all about what I have learned on my journey. I'm writing it from memory alone (that should be interesting); I don't want to consult books as then I would be using other people's words when I really just want to write it from my heart.

I'm not sure where it will take me, or even if it will make an interesting read, but here goes.

Life seems to go along as it's meant to, with its ups and downs. Nothing is ever wasted, whether it's the ups or the downs. We always learn from it, then carry on going along our path.

CHAPTER 1

THINGS THAT I HAVE FOUND HELPFUL WITH ME

I have spaced this section out so that it's easier to process. I know how hard it is to take in information with a woolly ME brain.

My sister Karen introduced me to her friend Angel, who has ME. We text and sometimes call each other. We each know how the other feels. Unless you have ME, you can't really understand what we are going through, so it's so lovely that we have each other. She's such a valued friend.

If you have the Internet I'm sure Facebook has a page for ME – a place to find a friend and people that understand how you are feeling.

It really does help.

Observe your emotional reactions to certain situations. My big one was if I needed to have two consecutive long days – doctors, hospital appointments, etc. After the first day I would begin to feel mildly anxious about finding the energy for the next day. Would I feel strong/well enough?

The last time that I felt this I thought, 'I have had this same reaction for so long; can I deal with this differently?'

Sit with that feeling. Gently breathe in and out. Say, "Thank you, anxiety, for your concern, but I need to release you for now." Still gently breathing, replace it with a calm, warm, soothing it-will-be-OK feeling.

Anxiety has its place, but it can be all-consuming at times.

Acceptance. I used to be a very busy person before ME, always on the go, here, there and everywhere. This seems to be the case with people that I have spoken to that have ME. For a long time I pined to have that life back again.

Gradually I began to realise that I liked my more peaceful, calm life and wouldn't ever want to go back to that way of living again. We really do need that balance.

I know now how easy it is to catch so many things, so try not to let yourself get too cold. When your body temperature drops, it lowers your immune system.

Warming clothes on the radiator in the winter before putting them on is so, so soothing for painful bodies. It's just like a warm hug. I used to do it for my children when they were young, and now do it for my two small grandsons, Coby and Kai, when they come over for a sleepover. They love it too.

Warming tea helps my inside feel warm, especially tea containing chopped ginger. There is a 'spice mix' box of teabags that I buy containing cinnamon, ginger and cardamom. I usually buy them when they are part of a 'buy one, get one half-price' offer as they aren't that cheap.

Also I ask for things like that, that I can't usually afford, for birthday and Christmas presents.

A notebook is a good thing to have. In mine I write anything that I need to remember. I keep it handy when I'm on the phone as I can guarantee that I will think of something that I need to say whilst the other person is talking; I can't remember what it was by the time I get to speak unless I scribble it down.

Also if I have somebody coming to visit I write down anything that I need to say to them. If all my children are visiting together I have lists under 'Danny', 'Terry', 'Sam' and, my daughter-in-law, 'Gem'.

My shopping list is so important too. ME affects my brain the most. I say that it's like how your head feels when you have the worst flu. That's how mine is nearly all the time.

I'm not sure how I'm managing to write this book. Divine intervention maybe?

I can no longer drive as my head is not clear enough to concentrate on driving. My reactions aren't quick enough. Crossing the road on foot is bad enough. I found out that if your health condition affects your driving, you can temporarily give your driving licence in and then apply for a disabled concessionary bus pass from your local authority. They will send you a form to fill in.

My life has opened up since I received mine. It is one of my most prized possessions.

Walking into town was too much for me, so I stayed at home most of the time. I am now able to ride into town and even go on a trip just to see a bit of countryside somewhere, then hop back on a bus to come back home.

If you are on a benefit and have a hospital appointment

you can claim your train or bus fares or petrol mileage back. You will need to show your benefit letter. Reception at the hospital will be able to advise you where to go. There is usually a cashier's office there.

For eleven years a friend of mine with ME went to numerous hospital appointments without knowing this, so I thought that it was worth mentioning.

I can't sleep if my body is cold, so I always take a hot-water bottle to bed with me on chilly nights and wear cosy bedsocks.

Eating regularly can help. My energy drops quite rapidly if I leave too many hours between eating; so I now have breakfast, lunch and dinner, then in between have a healthy snack, such as a handful of nuts or oatcakes with hummus, sugar-free jam or nut butter.

Nuts can be expensive, but I find some supermarkets have reasonably priced packs.

I know that organic is best, but that's not usually possible on a low budget. I feel as long as you are doing the best you can with food, that's all anyone can ask.

If you have digestive problems, make sure that that area is really relaxed before you eat. Then, after you have eaten, sit up so that you aren't slumped and keep relaxed for ten to fifteen minutes if possible.

I do find that my appetite isn't that great at times. Then I struggle to eat much at teatime. At one time I found that I was waking up in the middle of the night unable to sleep, and almost buzzing. Not long ago I came to realise that I felt hungry at that time. Now if I can't eat very much for my evening meal, then I have a couple of oatcakes or a small bowl of porridge before I go to bed.

It really helps, keeping my blood sugar levels up.

Don't be too hard on yourself. It is hard when you have to let someone down through not feeling so great, but it really isn't your fault that you can't make it. I'm sure that's a feeling many people with ME experience.

Changing my diet has helped to relieve some of my symptoms. This is a personal choice, and I can't say this would be right for everyone.

As I was aware which food affected me I was able to withdraw them from my diet to see if it helped.

Gluten not only bloats me, but also causes my joints and muscles to feel very painful.

I get a very upset and painful digestive system with dairy.

Sugar gives me an instant very painful headache.

I have read books from the library about replacement foods. Therefore I eat a really good, varied diet, and I still eat bread, cakes and biscuits which I make myself. We all need tasty treats now and then, don't we? I'm building up quite a collection of lovely recipes that I have adapted to suit me.

Although I am sharing this with you and it has worked really well for me, if you feel maybe there are certain foods that you are sensitive to please seek professional advice.

I am also vegetarian because of my love of animals.

I am also very sensitive to medication. The side effects I experience are far worse than whatever I have taken the medication for in the first place! Hence my search for alternative ways of dealing with my symptoms.

I can't sit in a room for too long with Wi-Fi on, as I start to feel drained and sick and my head goes numb, almost dead inside.

The same with talking on a mobile or cordless phone.

I have a corded phone, no Internet and keep text messages to a minimum. I also have no electrical appliances or mobile phone in my bedroom at all.

It does seem to be that many people with ME are ultra-sensitive to many things.

When I first moved to my current house I became very unwell, and Amy suggested that I could have geopathic stress (GS) in my home. She asked me to draw a plan of my bedroom and send it to Rolf Gordon, Dulwich Health, as if you are sleeping in a GS area it affects your health greatly.

It turned out that I was, and he suggested where to move my bed to. I was then able to sleep a lot better. He does this for free.

There's too much on this subject to write here, and I also can't describe it in simple terms, but please look on his website. There's lots of information. Or if you phone he will send it to you for free.

I have included his details at the back of this book.

Alternative therapies can be very beneficial, although they can be expensive. Colleges and training centres always need people to practice on at a small cost. I live near an international college of oriental medicine. They do acupuncture treatments for free, so it's worth looking to see what's in your area.

Gentle Massage

Gem is an amazing aromatherapist. She is very gentle, which is wonderful for my body when it is feeling so painful. Massage seems to release the pain. My body becomes so relaxed. I feel like I'm floating when she has finished!

BLISS. Gem is highly recommended!

Massage and aromatherapy students always need case studies, usually for free or a small donation.

Reiki

My good friend Gill is a wonderful reiki healer, and I have had a few sessions with her. I feel so light, pain-free and totally blissful during my session. After one session she said, "Look in the mirror."

My eyes, usually very dull, had come alive and were sparkling. I felt so relaxed.

Often people that have Reiki 1 Attunement need people to practise on.

Counselling

Counselling can be very helpful. It might not be for everyone, but it can help. It's a safe, confidential space in which to explore concerns, thoughts and feelings that arise connected with ME.

I was fortunate to have some free sessions from Dee, a lovely lady who was nearing the end of her counselling training. I felt very supported, and I was able to say just what I wanted to without feeling judged.

I learned to understand and value myself, also that I am not responsible for everyone's happiness and guilt is anger turned inwards!

When I've had a very unwell day in the past, I have felt almost fearful, thinking 'Oh no, not again!' That feeling sinks right down into me.

When that happens I relax my body and release the sinking feeling back up again and out of my body. Then I look down inside with kindness, and I let that feeling float down instead.

Once I had worked on my self-love/compassion I was able to easily change that feeling to treat my body with kindness, telling myself it's OK.

See Chapter 7 for exercises to do.

If you feel too much pressure in your head, stand with your feet firmly on the floor and let that energy drop down and out through your feet into the ground.

Whilst lying or sitting, picture bright white light coming into the top of your head and filling up every part of your body from head to toe. Do this whenever you think of it.

It helps you to feel brighter and lighter inside.

It's one of my favourite things to do. If you choose only one thing to do, try this. It is so beneficial.

Drawing when you are angry, upset, frustrated or even happy is a great way to express your feelings.

Paper and a pencil are all you need. Crayons and felt tips can be used to add colour. I have a junior set of oil pastels.

Scribbling furiously when I am feeling angry is so very therapeutic and a great release.

It's surprising what you can achieve when you just go with the emotion you are feeling.

I recently had a breakthrough when I was staying with my parents. They had both been in hospital with chronic chest infections. My health had suffered and my body was so painful from sleeping on a fold-up bed.

On the day I was going home it was a fraught morning. All sorts of things went wrong. I was wondering just how I was going to manage a three-hour, four-buses journey home.

My son Terry and his fiancée, Monica, had popped in to see us the evening before and had given his grandparents a late Christmas present. It was a CD of songs from musicals.

Mum decided they wanted to play it late morning. We all sat with our eyes closed – well, Mum did after she had read the paper! It was amazing, the calm that came over me, just sitting listening to it.

It stayed with me all the way home. By the time I got

back I realised I wasn't in even half as much pain as I usually felt, and not so shattered either.

It just goes to show that listening to soothing music does wonders to reduce pain, even it it's only for a short while.

My daughter, Sam, gave me a bottle of Aura Clear Spray for a present. It's good to use if you have been with negative people, or even on public transport, where there are so many different energies. You just spray it in your aura.

Write down all of your gifts and the positive qualities that you have, however small, to remind yourself how wonderful you truly are.

Visualise then write down how you would like your life to be. Really feel it.

What do I desire from life?

It's interesting to read this back a month, six months or a year later to see how different your life is, and if that is still the life you desire.

If you are a reiki healer, or any other sort of spiritual healer, place your hands on an area that is painful and let the energy flow.

Even if you aren't a healer, place your hands on there anyway, as warm hands are very soothing. Or even ask your partner, parent or friend to try this on you. You might be pleasantly surprised.

When you get a day when you wake up feeling that you

have more energy, it's so easy to think, 'Yey! I can do so much today,' then give it all away.

Be kind to yourself. Do a little bit of floor washing, cleaning, ironing, etc., then sit and do something you love to do, or even sit with your eyes closed to relax for a while.

It's so, so easy to keep going, thinking, 'I must do all of this,' then crashing, with all of your energy draining away!

This is a more gentle be-kind-to-yourself approach.

Imagine that you have an 'energy bank'. Every time you feel that you have some energy, rather than using it all up, save some, so that it starts to build you up, stronger and stronger.

Balance your life by reducing the need to be perfect – expecting too much of yourself, being self-critical, overworking – and increasing the love that you give yourself. Accept who you are, be aware of what's needed to boost your self-esteem and learn to say no!

This will go a long way to help you to feel calmer and more centred.

I came to realise that I almost constantly felt like I had a motor running inside me. It never seemed to switch off!

I have been told in the past that I was an anxious person, although on the surface I wouldn't have said that I was.

So if this motor was always running, this in itself must have caused extreme fatigue!

Angel (who suffers from severe anxiety at times) tells me that whenever she has been away on holiday, she feels that all her symptoms disappear until she gets home again.

This leads me to believe that relaxation is a very important factor in helping to alleviate some ME symptoms.

Visualisation for Pain Relief

Sit or lie (whichever you are comfortable doing). Slow your breathing. Connect with your breath, placing a hand on your stomach if you like. Visualise a really sunny day with the gentle sun shining down on you, feeling the warmth.

Now take your focus down into where you can feel the pain.

Allow the gentle warmth of the sun to gradually fill the painful area. Let it bathe, comfort, warm, relax.

With each breath bring in more warmth. Fill the painful area with warmth until it begins to soothe and relax.

If it's your whole body that's painful, fill your whole being with warm, golden sunlight. Keep breathing it in until you feel warm all over.

Stay with this for as long as you want. When you learn how to access the warmth you can instantly connect with it when needed.

If you are standing at a bus stop or sitting in the garden on a sunny day, let the heat of the sun fill your body. It's a really lovely thing to do.

Visualisation to Help You Sleep or Relax

Breathe in through your nose slowly, then slowly out a few times to still your mind.

Bring your mind down into your body. Take your focus to your brain. Notice how it feels. Observe it. Don't change how it feels.

Then gradually work your way down your body, just observing, covering every part – eyes, ears, nose, cheeks, jaw, teeth, throat, down your arms and into your hands, shoulders, down through each lung, breast, thymus, heart, liver, digestive system, stomach, kidneys, pancreas, right down your legs and into your feet.

Next bring your attention to your skin. Travel down the outside with your focus, from head to toes, at the front of your body. Then do the same at the back of your body, including your arms and hands.

Stay in this stillness for a few moments, then reverse, travelling back up the inside of your body, revisiting all that you observed going down. Do the same with your skin, travelling back up.

This calms the body and mind.

You are important enough to matter.

Releasing Pain

Lie comfortably. Start at the top of your head, feel like it is sinking into the pillow. Feel your forehead relaxing, opening up, so that also sinks into the pillow.

Feel your eyes, jaws, throat, heart, stomach area, lower abdomen and base of spine all in turn opening up and sinking deep into the mattress.

When we are in pain, we huddle into ourselves. This exercise opens up our body, releases pain and gives energy to each part of our body.

CHAPTER 2

GROUNDING AND PROTECTION

Grounding and protection are very important. If you ground and protect yourself each time you do a deep meditation or visualisation, you will be secure within your own body. Check you are grounded afterwards as well to connect you back into yourself.

We need to be grounded to Mother Earth. She energises us. She stops us from floating up and living in our heads or above. She helps us to feel solid and secure.

Protection stops you picking up other people's energies or the energies of places which can drain you and affect how you feel.

Grounding Heaven to Earth

Stand relaxed. Breathe in slowly through your nose. As you do so, bring in a stream of bright white light from above down to your heart.

As you breathe out let the white light flow from your heart right down and out of your feet into the ground. Do this a few times until you really feel connected.

Stand relaxed. Visualise a column of gold light coming down and in through your head, travelling right down and out through your base chakra, and also down your legs and out through your feet, all three columns going deep into the ground.

Stand with your feet heavily on the floor. Picture strong roots from your feet going deep into Mother Earth.
    Having bare feet outside is very grounding too.

The Quickest Way to Ground

Stand with your feet apart. Place your hands together as if you are praying, elbows out to the side.
    Press your hands together firmly for a few seconds.
    You will feel your weight drop down into your feet and you may feel tingling. You will then feel like you are sinking right into the ground.
    So simple, yet so effective.

Protection

Visualise yourself standing in a bright white bubble. Fill your aura up with bright white light, cascading down from above your head.

Visualise violet-white flames coming up and around your body and over your head.

Protection: House, Car, Children

Visualise bright white light around each of your children and valued possessions. Fill your whole house up with white light.

I always ask Archangel Michael for protection, and I know he protects me.

Put a few drops of lavender essential oil in some spring water in a small spray bottle. Spray it around your aura for protection.

CHAPTER 3

CHAKRAS AND THE AURA

I am going to mention chakras and the aura briefly as they are part of our energy system.

Chakras are vortexes of spinning light, the energy centres for our well-being. There are seven main ones. Each one is a different colour.

The base chakra is red. It is situated at the base of your spine, pointing downwards.

The sacral chakra is orange. It is situated between the hip bones of your pelvis, just below your tummy button.

The solar plexus is yellow. It is situated one inch above your tummy button.

The heart chakra is green. It is situated in the centre of your chest.

The throat chakra is sky blue. It is situated in the centre of your throat.

The third eye is indigo. It is situated in the middle of your forehead.

The crown chakra is violet-white. It is situated at the top of your head, in line with your spine.

The aura is a protective energy field around your body.

I don't really have the words to describe either chakras or the aura fully, so it's best to go online or find a book in the library to read more about the subject.

Fragrant Flower Visualisation

Sit with a fragrant flower that you love in front of you.

Gently breathe in and out through your nose, inhaling the scent of your flower.

With every breath, feel the aroma filling your whole body.

Inhale the colour too, so that your whole being is, for example, pink and filled with the fragrance of roses. It really is a very beautiful thing to do.

CHAPTER 4

CREATING YOUR FAVOURITE PEACEFUL SANCTUARY

First on a piece of paper write down all that you would love to have in your peaceful place. It could be anywhere – beside the sea, on a tropical island, on a mountain, in a meadow or in a beautiful garden – anywhere that would be a blissful place to be.

Sit comfortably with your feet on the ground. Slow your breathing. Be really aware of it.

Bring your focus down into your body. Be aware of your stomach rising and falling.

Picture strong roots growing out of your feet deep down into the ground.

Feel Mother Earth's beautiful energy rising back up the roots into your feet, up your legs, through your abdomen and chest and over your shoulders then down your arms into your hands.

Feel the energy spreading up your neck and into your head until you are filled with her beauty.

Visualise or feel your peaceful place – how it looks and smells, and what you can hear. Let its beautiful energy envelop you. Feel the peace. Feel at one there. Sit there for a while, then bring your attention back to where you are sitting and thank Mother Earth for sharing her energy with you.

If you can't visualise it as a whole then imagine each part, telling yourself it's always there for you.

I couldn't visualise at all to begin with, so I do know that it can be a problem. It does come in the end; but until then, knowing and feeling is just as good.

This is a place you can access quickly once you get to know how it really feels to be there. Then you can connect with that feeling whenever you need to be calm and at peace, without having to do the whole visualisation.

CHAPTER 5

SELF-AWARENESS

This is where my journey began. I had an angel card reading many years ago. One of my questions was "How can I progress on my spiritual journey?" I was told to begin to be self-aware.

This has been a slow process, but when you are aware, in all aspects in your life, it's quite an eye-opener.

You really realise how different things affect you in your life and how to do the very best for yourself.

Positive thoughts make you feel better inside than negative ones.

Self-love, self-respect, self-worth.

Acceptance – feel deserving of what's being offered, such as help, friendship and gifts. Say, "I am worthy of this" or "I am worth it." Don't struggle on alone, always saying, "I'm OK – it's OK, I don't need help [or whatever's being offered]."

Also accept who you are. Never compare yourself to somebody else. We are all unique. We come with our own set of gifts.

Gradually you will begin to realise that negative things, such as newspaper stories, the news on TV, storylines in soaps and a lot of dramas, are not good for you. Their influence is quite dark. Being with negative people can bring you down. You can end up getting drawn into it all.

Being surrounded by positive and uplifting people, programmes and stories will lift your spirits and make your energy rise.

Ultimately, when inner peace is found, negative things won't affect you. That's not always easy though.

You know things that make your heart sing.

What's going on inside? Think about how things make you feel. You may have sensitivities to food, Wi-Fi, cleaning products or other people's energies. Perhaps there are behaviours/habits that no longer serve you. All these things can cause tension.

Be aware also of what makes you feel good, such as foods, places and people. Like-minded people/friends that you can share your thoughts and feelings with are so important. I call them food for my soul.

Awareness just grows and grows once you start. The right books and the right people appear. Synchronicities happen.

It seems that even your intuition grows too.

The world can become a very magical place.

CHAPTER 6

CHANGES/COMFORT ZONES

Routine has its place. It's lovely to be comfy, safe and set in your ways. But I've recently realised that I can't stay the way I live for the rest of my life – and as I am fifty-seven (nearly fifty-eight), that may be a good few years yet. Seeing as I have been doing the same things for the last thirteen years, maybe it's time for a change.

Something inside me is beginning to make me feel very uncomfortable. When I go to make one of my familiar meals, it's like something inside me screams, "No – please change what I am going to eat!" I just can't cook it.

Many of my old ways are now being challenged. If I try to do old, comfy things, they seem to go a bit pear-shaped, and I don't feel so good. I feel uneasy rather than relaxed.

If my bus doesn't turn up, so I have to walk, then I find that actually I enjoy the walk into town. It energises me!

I'm beginning to look through my cookbooks to find new recipes. Even one new recipe a week is good.

Sometimes I take myself off to bed really early as I don't have a TV licence any more, and I fall asleep at eight thirty. Lately I have been getting ideas for things to write about, and I'm actually stopped from sleeping until ten. It almost feels like I am coming out from a deep sleep, like a chrysalis turning into a butterfly. I can't slumber any more.

Could this be the same for many of you? Are you just playing safe?

Recently I was told of a Festival of Light spiritual event in town. Entry was free and all of the workshops and talks were free too. The bus could get me there at just the right time, so I had no excuses not to go.

I sat on my bed, thinking, 'Shall I go? No – I will have to be sociable. I'm not interesting enough to hold a proper conversation. People will be watching me. It's too much effort. I don't feel that well . . .' All the usual excuses!

I decided my bed felt much more comfortable and cosy, so I decided not to go.

I picked up a book that I hadn't looked at for a long time: *Light is the New Black* by Rebecca Campbell. The title on the page was 'Your Greatest Fear Is the Gatekeeper to Your Highest Calling'.

That's all I needed to push me to go.

I had such a great time. I met up with Paula Adams, who had a stand, doing chakra readings for a donation for charity. She told me my throat chakra needed working on. She also said I was going to write a book! And I would have my own stand there next year.

I had a free mini reading from Maxine Temple (who has such a beautiful soul, and is a very talented medium) because I had recommended my sister and a friend, who had paid for readings from her.

A lot came up from that reading for me to digest. One thing was that, I am extremely hard on myself. Until I was told that I hadn't realised just how much I am.

I also met another wonderful lady – Jeanette. We are like two peas in a pod; we have so many similarities and we spent the rest of the day together just talking and talking.

This is an entry I wrote in my journal a few days later.

Have come to realise today that I am changing my old habits, behaviours that no longer serve me. Eleven years ago (on 8 December) I was diagnosed with ME. When I feel rough and weary I lie on my bed. I have been told in the past that going out into nature will revive me, but I have never been able to do that.

Just lately, when I have lain down to rest my weary body, I have had an energy appear within that doesn't feel that great. The realisation is that I have done this for so long that it is time for a change.

Maybe my soul is getting bored of doing things the same way.

Went into myself, away from my mind and asked if I should in fact go out. It was a resounding yes!

I thought that I would go to Standen to see the Christmas tree. It was so cold out, but I was determined to go – listening to my heart and not my head, which was saying something completely different.

I sat at the bus stop. The first bus that came along would have taken me home and it was tempting to get on, but I waited for the bus I needed. And it was so worth it.

The energy at Standen was so beautiful. It was dusk when I got there. I was very brave and didn't feel lonely at all. I took some amazing photos of the sunset on my way back up the lane to catch the bus.

I was only there for an hour, but I felt so different when I came home.

I have to start doing different things. My soul needs variety.

National Trust membership, paid monthly by direct debit, is a great incentive to get out and connect with nature. Many National Trust properties are accessible by bus for those who, like me, are no longer able to drive.

Change can be accomplished in small ways, like trying a new recipe each week. You can change the colour or the style of the clothes you wear, or change how you think about things, or watch a TV programme or film that you normally wouldn't consider seeing. Be brave – try something you haven't done before.

The sense of achievement, however small, is well worth it.

CHAPTER 7

COMPASSION

We can only find compassion by loving ourselves first.

The greatest gift I gave myself was to feel compassion for all parts of me, positive and negative.

At one time, every time it was needed I just froze and blocked it out. I didn't have or feel compassion towards myself, so how could I feel this for others?

The way I began to combat this was to start treating myself kindly.

If this is you also, this is what I recommend:

Treat yourself as you would a treasured member of your family or a friend.

When things go wrong, give yourself a hug and say, "It's OK. You're OK."

Perform small acts of kindness to yourself. If you are saying no to yourself, think, 'Would I say no to my son/daughter, partner or friend?' For example, put the heating on, run a bath, buy yourself a bunch of daffodils or a small bar of chocolate, or curl up with a book. You really do deserve the best.

It really is a lovely feeling when you start recognising your self-worth.

Say to yourself, "I am worthy of this."

If I start to push myself too hard, or treat myself in any way unkindly, I think, 'Would I treat someone I love like this?'

Only when I started to feel love and compassion for myself, could I then really feel it for others.

It's so easy to criticise ourselves for eating something we shouldn't. Change that feeling to one of kindness. It's OK to enjoy every mouthful, rather than eating it with loathing and fear.

When an emotion comes up that you don't feel too comfortable with, sit with it, acknowledge it.
  Look inwards kindly, saying, "It's OK. I can feel you." Treat it with kindness, love and acceptance, as if it were a small child.
  Don't try to change it. Just sit with it, accepting that it's one of your emotions. It's part of you.

Once we love all our emotions – all parts of ourselves – the compassion will grow.

If you eat, drink or smoke to squash down or numb extremely painful emotions or feelings, try this: when the painful emotion comes up, focus your mind on that feeling.

Be aware of your breath, slowly breathing in and out.

Start to feel tenderness towards that emotion as you would to a small child. Say, "It's OK. I can feel you. I will help you," all the time breathing slowly.

Keep feeling kindness and talking, saying anything soothing and encouraging that you can think of. Just acknowledge that feeling/emotion.

Gradually it will start to subside. Keep going – it may take up to twenty minutes.

This sort of emotion is usually something that's been buried. It needs to be released.

Don't worry if this technique doesn't work the first, second or third time and you have to eat something to relieve it. I know how hard it is. The feeling can be so, so overwhelming that you just need to drink, eat or smoke to make it go away.

Don't give up. Keep persevering. It will be released in the end.

It's a massive achievement once you have managed this.

I do feel that the more our darker emotions are ignored, the stronger they come up until they are recognised.

Thank You: Gratitude to All Body Parts

Lie down. Breathe consciously to still your mind. Bring your focus down into your body.

Starting with your brain, say, 'Thank you, brain, for helping me think today,' or anything else you feel that it has done for you. Then work your way down your body, thanking each part for what it does. Each part feels really grateful to be acknowledged and thanked.

Our bodies work really hard for us.

Forgiving Yourself

There are things in life that we have all done that we aren't proud of.

Sit quietly. Say to yourself, 'Please forgive me for . . . [whatever it is that you need forgiveness for].'

Next say, 'I forgive myself.'

Know that you are forgiven. Give yourself a big hug. Then sit for a couple of minutes.

This can be very powerful.

Be proud of who you are.

CHAPTER 8

JOURNALS

A journal is a great thing to write. Sometimes you really forget what has been written, and you find yourself looking back over it at a time when what's written resounds within.

My son Danny gave me a journal for my birthday last year, and looking back over the year I realise how much I had forgotten.

It's great for writing all your thoughts, worries, concerns and achievements. You can rant in it, cry and laugh, and it will always be there for you.

Some of what I wrote in my journal I am using in this book.

It's like talking things over with a best friend. The process of writing is quite releasing – it saves things being bottled up inside.

My very first entry, written on my birthday, was

I've woken this morning feeling like something has been released – fear maybe? I no longer worry about how much gas, electricity, water I use. Careful, but with ease rather than fear.

Staying consciously within my body. Calm. Live life consciously not through emotions.

The next day's entry began 'Woke up with overwhelming fear!' That's how much things change from day to day.

Dreams are good to record in there too. I would never have remembered any if I hadn't written them down. I have some pretty amazing and meaningful ones at times.

Before I had my journal, I had notebooks and even scraps of paper. It really doesn't matter where you write – it's releasing it all that counts.

We walk in our thoughts. They pave the way.

CHAPTER 9

THINGS THAT MAKE YOUR HEART SING

Things that make your heart sing or make you smile are so important in life. They give you that feel-good feeling. We all need some of that each day. It can be anything.

Watching children playing. Being with family or close friends. Having a bubble bath with candles. Watching pets, or birds in the garden. Enjoying a favourite film or TV programme. . . .

There's a male childminder that always makes me smile when I see him. He's either like the Pied Piper, with children all around him, or when he's walking to collect a child, or on his way home, he walks along reading a book. He seems a delightful soul.

Going to the cinema is also something that makes my heart sing, partly because I go with Sam. Also it's a great way to lose yourself, immersed in a film.

Sometimes when I have been out to feed the birds I come back inside and Perry, the cat from next door, has invited himself in and is wandering round. He lifts my spirit.

There are so many delights in life if you look for them. Anything that you love just lifts your spirit and boosts your morale a little bit.

Appreciate yourself and honour your soul.

CHAPTER 10

MEDITATION

It's quite amazing when you get stuck for an answer and then it comes right out of the blue.

One day when I was talking to a friend on the phone, she suddenly started to tell me how when she went to a new meditation group the teacher told people new to it, and maybe feeling a bit fearful of getting it right, how to still their minds.

We hadn't even been talking about that subject! It was perfect as it reminded me of a way I have done it at times.

I thought about Bev when I started to write about meditation as she had asked me a few times how to meditate.

I'm not that great at going into the kind of meditative state where you have wonderful things happen; I just go within to my inner stillness.

Sitting comfortably, with your feet on the floor, breathe in and out slowly through your nose.

Put your hand on your tummy.

Bring your mind down inside to where your hands are resting, and focus on them going up and down.

If any thoughts come into your mind, just bring your focus back down to your hands again.

Sit for five minutes doing this to start with. It isn't easy to still your mind at first, when it's been used to thinking about so many things.

Anything that quietens your mind is good to take it from your worries. Even doing this for a few seconds at a time to start with can leave you feeling calmer.

Really studying an object is another way – for example, look at your hand as if you were just seeing it for the first time. Notice the colour, texture, lines and veins. See how it moves, how long your fingers are. Look at the nails. Feel fascinated by this 'new' object.

This can be done with anything. Look around the room that you are sitting or lying in.

If you really study something you will find that you don't have any other thoughts. It's a very interesting thing to do.

Babies are wonderful to observe. They make amazing facial expressions even when asleep.

A pet would be another good one, perhaps when it is lying or sitting down.

Sitting or lying with your eyes closed, listening to soothing music stills your mind. It doesn't have to be classical music, which personally I struggle to listen to.

My favourite CD is *Requiem Well of Souls* by Nigel Shaw. I get so lost in his music – he is an amazing man. I have met him a few times. He gives lovely bear hugs. He lives with his wife, Carolyn Hillyer, on Dartmoor. They are a very talented couple, running workshops, festivals and much more. Their website is really worth a look.

Walking Meditation

Walking through a wood or along an unmade path, really feel your feet on the ground, almost sinking in, connecting with Mother Earth as you slowly walk.

Be aware of your breathing.

Take in all that's around you – the grass, the ground under your feet, trees, flowers, water, the air, the gentle wind, the sun. What can you hear? Birds, water trickling, branches blowing in the wind? Be at one with nature. Walk like this for as long as you want to.

Even sitting on a bus you can make a connection with nature.

The bus I sometimes take goes across Ashdown Forest. The views are breathtaking. I always feel peaceful taking it all in.

Being in the moment is a good way to still your mind. When you are washing up really look at what you are doing. Notice how clean each thing is as it's being washed – how warm the water feels.

While doing anything, from having a shower to cleaning or gardening, focus on only that thing; don't also think about what to make for dinner or when your next appointment is.

I was cooking dinner and was so busy thinking of helpful things to write in my book, at the same time, that the coconut oil I was heating got rather hot!

That will teach me to practise what I preach. I am only human – that's my excuse anyway.

Qigong and yoga are gentle, and great for stilling the mind and finding the stillness within.

CHAPTER 11

CLEANSING THE ENERGIES IN THE HOME

Stagnant energies can build up in our homes. Buy a bundle of sage – sometimes called a smudge stick. They can usually be found in shops selling crystals, incense sticks and candles.

Light a candle, then light the sage from the candle. It will start to smoulder. Put it on a saucer.

Let the smoke from the sage fill every corner of the room as you slowly walk up and down. A feather can be good to waft the smoke around too.

Say, "I transmute all stagnant energy and transform it into love and light."

Also let the smoke flow into your aura. It's cleansing and very calming.

CHAPTER 12

ROSE QUARTZ HEART VISUALISATION

Sit comfortably with your feet firmly on the floor. Take some deep breaths to still yourself. Take your focus down inside to your feet.

Picture roots coming out of them and travelling deep into the ground, going down and down until they meet the most beautiful, glowing, very large rose-quartz crystal.

Wrap your roots around it and very slowly bring the beautiful pink energy back up through your roots, up into your feet. Feel this beautiful pale-pink slowly rise up through your feet, ankles, calves and knees, flowing up through your thighs, and hips into your abdomen, all the way up to your shoulders. See the pink flowing down your arms into your hands. Fill your back and chest.

Finally bring this lovely pink up your neck to the top of your head. Keep bringing it up until your whole body is filled with amazing pink, loving light.

Bring your focus to your heart and fill it with this beautiful loving pink energy until it feels so full of love.

Sit with this for as long as you want to, then bring your mind back to the seat you are sitting on.

CHAPTER 13

NEW MOON WISHES

Find out what day and time the new moon is.

Write down wishes for yourself. This can be done at new moon and for up to two days after it.

Repeat the wishes often. This really does work. If you find some don't come true, it could be because something else needs to be done before they can. I usually wish things for my personal growth. I've never asked to win the lottery. Maybe I should!

If you have a decision to make or can't find an answer to something, sit quietly, relax into your body. Speaking to your heart, ask the question again. See what comes up.

CHAPTER 14

ANGELS AND ARCHANGELS

I love to connect with angels and archangels. I can feel their beautiful energies.

Even if you can't, if you have called them, just know that they heard your call and are there with you.

Ask them to wrap their beautiful wings around you, and always say thank you when they have done so.

I have friends who always ask for the Parking Angel to find them a parking space, and it always seems to work.

Ask the angels of light to put protection around loved ones' cars if they are going to be out late at night – or any time you feel they need that extra help.

Danny works nights, and I often ask for protection around his car when he's driving home in the morning after work, and also when he's at work, as he works alone.

White feathers are angels' calling cards. I often find feathers in the strangest of places.

Archangel Metatron Chakra Balancing

Sit or lie comfortably.

Say, "I call upon Archangel Metatron. Please could you use your geometric sphere to cleanse and balance my chakras. Thank you."

Stay still awhile. Feel each chakra vibrate a little. If you don't feel it, just know it is happening.

Call upon the angels to give you strength when you need it.

If you feel a bit down, sit quietly and say, "I call upon Archangel Michael. Please could you take all the negative thoughts, feelings, energies and emotions that have been sent my way? Turn them into white light and love, then send them back to where they came from. Thank you."

Breathe deeply and stay still for a few minutes. You should feel your energy begin to brighten again.

Aura Clearing

We can pick up bits in our auras. The following is a good technique to keep them clear.

Sit or lie quietly, breathing slowly.

Say, "I call upon the angels. Please could you take any other parts of other people's auras that I have in mine, cleanse and heal them and send them back to where they belong."

Picture a very large comb, wider than yourself. Comb from the top of your head, down your front to under your feet. Imagine there is a big white light Hoover on the floor. Use this to hoover what the comb has picked up, then do the same to the back.

After a few minutes, say, "Please can you take any parts of me that other people have, cleanse and heal them and bring them back to me? Also, please could you mend any tears or holes in my aura? Thank you.

It's a really lovely feeling after it has all been done.

Cord Cutting: Laying Down

Say, "I call upon Archangel Michael. Please could you cut and dissolve all cords of fear that are draining my energy and vitality? Please can you cut and dissolve any cords that I have sent to other people and fill them with love and light. Replace pain with peace. Thank you."

Archangel Michael can be called upon to wrap his blue wings around you for protection.

Archangel Raphael can be called upon to wrap his emerald-green wings around you for healing.

If you get overwhelmed by too many things going on that you can't deal with, surrender and say, "Please help, dear angels. I can't do this any more. I'm handing it over to you. Thank you."

Then just let it all go out of your mind.

CHAPTER 15

EMBRACING ALL OUR EMOTIONS

Paula Adams is a beautiful, powerful Brennan healer, based in East Grinstead. She's very kind and compassionate.

I've learned such a lot from her. One of Paula's questions was "Where do you feel your anger?"

I didn't actually know!

She said, "Your feelings are all sitting outside of you."

Because I wasn't grounded a lot of the time, most of what I felt was outside of me or in my head.

I had developed a coping/defence mechanism from childhood, which came with me to adulthood, where I either blocked my emotions altogether or sort of took myself almost out of my body, so that I couldn't feel any of the negative stuff – it couldn't hurt.

Paula said all of our emotions are part of who we are.

I soon came to realise that I was happy to feel all of my good feelings, but didn't want to acknowledge the bad ones.

As a child, being good is what adults expect of you. They like good children. Children mustn't shout, get angry or express any other negative emotions.

I have observed young children being told off when negative feelings are shown or even for crying; therefore it's not surprising when they shut these feelings away and in the end find them hard to express.

When Paula was telling me about expressing all emotions, I was very defensive about it all.

"I don't feel negative emotions," I said. "They aren't part of me. I don't like the way they make me feel!"

I had a lot to learn. It took a good year or so before I began to accept what she was saying. See Chapter 7 for details of how I combated this.

I really needed to feel emotions within my body. I was aware that I was feeling them mostly in my head.

Paula also gave me an affirmation that I have said many times and still do now:

"I am important enough to matter."

I was also treated to a walking meditation with Paula one summer solstice. We did a slow meditation walk across some fields near to where she lives – all alone, but as a group. We ended up holding hands around a big old oak tree.

She led a short meditation.

Just connecting with nature and with the energy of the group was a truly amazing experience.

It is my favourite meditation of all time so far.

She also holds workshops and leads meditation groups.

I wanted to include a piece about Paula as I would never have embraced all of my emotions without her help. The knowledge that she gave me has helped me immensely to explore ways to help myself.

Thank you, Paula.

For all of you precious souls with ME/chronic fatigue, I am hoping this book has been a fairly easy read. I know that trying to get your brain to absorb anything is quite taxing.

I could only read half a page at a time when I was first diagnosed.

If this is you, maybe you could get a family member or friend to gradually read it to you. Even just Chapter 1 may be helpful.

I was there once. Now I have written a whole book!

So please feel hope that you will slowly recover and – who knows? – maybe even write your own story.

My love and blessings,
Trina

CONTACTS

Gemma Chapman
www.facebook.com/gemsmassagetherapies

Maxine Temple
mtemple@hotmail.co.uk

Denise Longhurst
www.deniselonghurst.co.uk

Festival of Light
www.spiritualawakeningcommunity.com

Rebecca Campbell
www.rebeccacampbell.me

Rolf Gordon
www.dulwichhouse.co.uk

Nigel Shaw
www.seventhwavemusic.co.uk